Fuel and Energy

Words by Herta S. Breiter

formerly Research Chemist
University of Illinois

Raintree Childrens Books
Milwaukee • Toronto • Melbourne • London

Library of Congress Number: 77-18560

4 5 6 7 8 9 0 82 81 80

Printed and bound in the United States of America.

Library of Congress Cataloging in Publication Data

Breiter, Herta S.
  Fuel and Energy.

  (Read about)
  Bibliography: p.
  Includes index.
  SUMMARY: An introduction to the location and
uses of various types of fuel and sources of energy.
  1. Fuel—Juvenile literature. 2. Power
resources—Juvenile literature. [1. Fuel.
2. Force and energy. 3. Power resources]
I. Title.
TP318.M67   333.7   77-18560
ISBN 0-8393-0083-2 lib. bdg.

Fuel and
Energy

Energy is the ability to do work. Anything that does work has energy. People work. Animals work. And the sun works to pull water from lakes and seas into the air. People, animals, and the sun all have energy.

There are different kinds of energy.
Light and heat are two kinds of energy.
The sun gives us both light and heat. It
helps make plants grow. It keeps people
and animals warm.

Long ago, people had no heat or light
after the sun went down. Then they found
out how to make fire. Wood is a fuel.
Anything that burns is a fuel. Fuels have
energy. The foods we eat have energy.
Foods are fuel for our bodies.

It took a lot of food energy to build the pyramids. But using rollers made the work easier. Long poles, called levers, also helped move the load. Rollers, levers, and ramps are called simple machines. A machine is something that makes work easier.

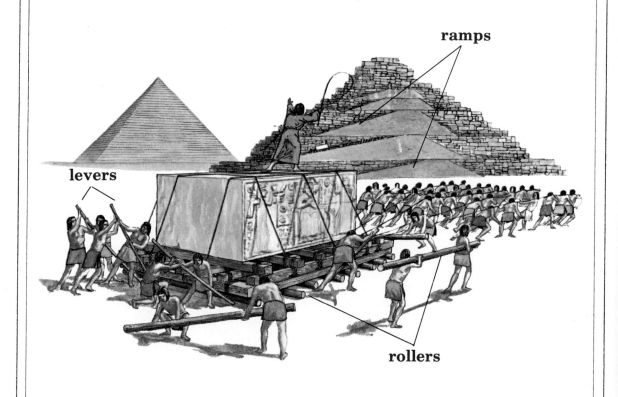

ramps

levers

rollers

6

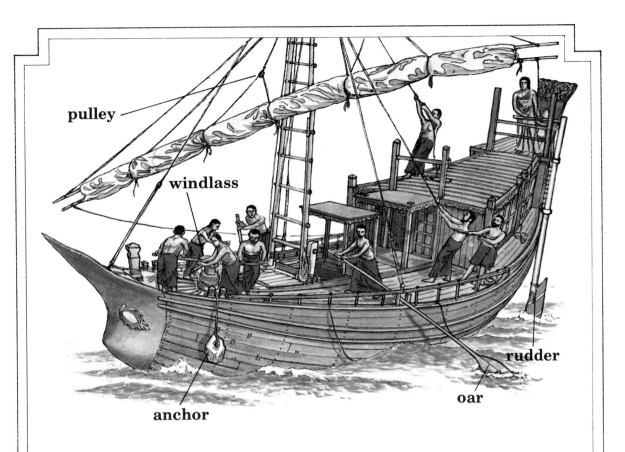

pulley

windlass

anchor

rudder

oar

   These sailors are using many simple
machines. The oars are levers that pull the
ship forward. The rudder is a lever that
steers the ship. The sailors are raising the
anchor with a windlass, which is a kind of
wheel. They are raising the sails with
pulleys. Machines make work easier.

Moving water has energy we can use to make work easier. The water moves over the waterwheel and makes it turn. The wheel turns an axle that hits a trip-hammer. The hammer pounds hot iron into shape. The axle also moves the bellows that blows air onto the fire.

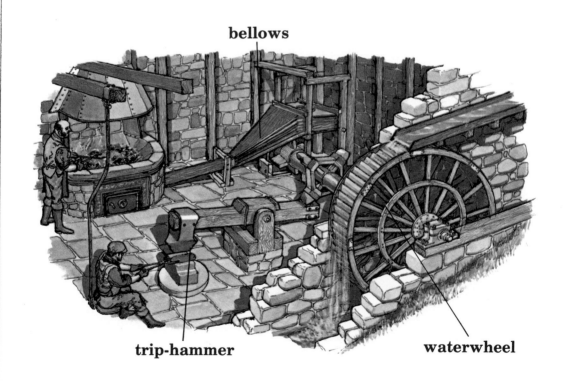

bellows

trip-hammer

waterwheel

Anything that is moving is doing work, so it has energy. Wind is moving air, so it has energy. People have long used the energy of wind. They built windmills to pump water or grind grain.

This mill grinds grain. The wind turns its sails. The sails turn gears. One of these gears turns a grindstone. The grindstone grinds grain into flour. Fantails keep the sails facing the wind.

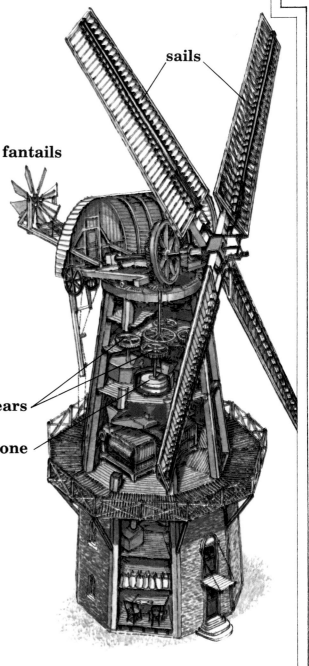

sails

fantails

gears

grindstone

Fuels are materials that give us energy. There are many kinds of fuels. Most of them come out of the earth. Coal is an important fuel. It was formed long ago from trees that died and fell into swamps. The trees sank and heavy rocks pressed on them. After millions of years, these trees turned into coal.

Oil is another important fuel. It is buried deep in the earth. It, too, was formed millions of years ago. Scientists think oil came from tiny sea creatures called diatoms. When diatoms died, they sank, and mud and rock covered them. The weight of folds of rock changed the diatoms to oil. The oil remained trapped deep in the earth.

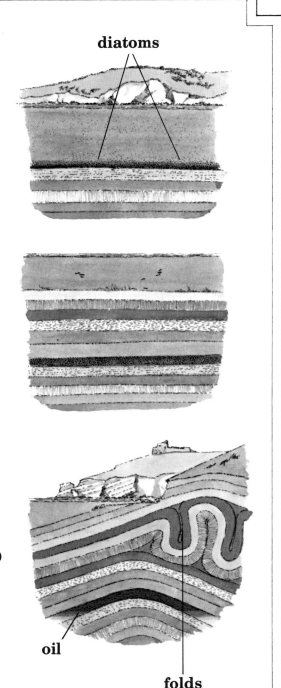

Fuels cannot help us if they stay deep in the earth. People needed these fuels, so they found ways of getting them. At first, they dug small holes called bell pits.

an old coal mine or "bell pit"

Modern mines have deep shafts that connect the surface with the coal seam. Most of the hard work is done with machines.

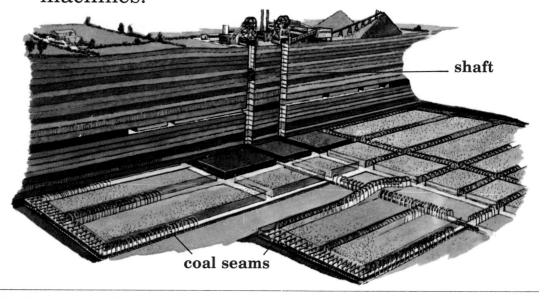

shaft

coal seams

pit props

coal on
conveyor belt

cutter

Digging for coal is dangerous and dirty. Miners run machines that cut the coal. A conveyor belt carries the coal to the shaft. Elevators carry the coal up the shaft. Pit props hold up the roof of the mine. Without these props, the roof could fall in.

This is an early steam engine. The energy that made it move came from burning coal. The fire changed the water in the boiler to steam. The steam pushed a piston, and the piston moved the wooden beams. When the beams moved, the big wheel turned. Steam engines pumped water out of mines. They also lifted coal up the shafts.

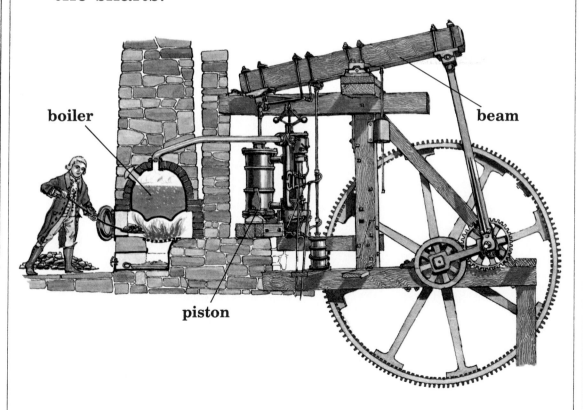

boiler

beam

piston

Steam engines also ran ships, trains, and factory and farm machinery. These ships and trains traveled quickly and safely. They were used all over the world. They could go as far as the coal they carried would allow them to go.

Coal can give us another fuel, called gas. Two hundred years ago, a scientist heated coal in a kettle without air. Gas came out. This coal gas could burn.

Later, coal gas was used to light homes and streets. Now it is used mostly by industries for heating buildings and for cooking.

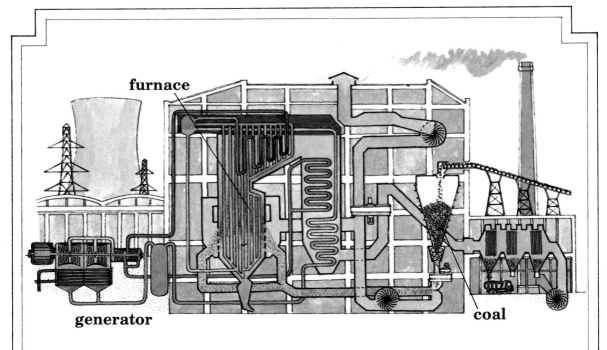

furnace

generator

coal

Coal can be used to make electrical energy. Coal is burned in a furnace. It heats water to make steam to turn a turbine. The turbine turns a generator. The generator makes electricity.

generator

steam in here

low pressure turbines

The energy of moving water can be changed into electricity. First, a high dam is built across a river to form a deep lake. Water behind the dam is sent through pipes to turbines in a power station. Each turbine turns a generator. The generator makes electrical energy.

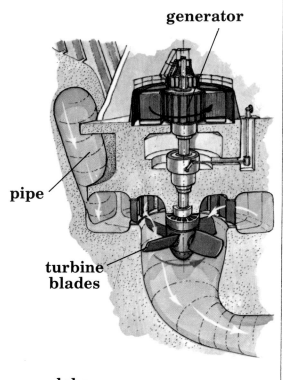

generator

pipe

turbine blades

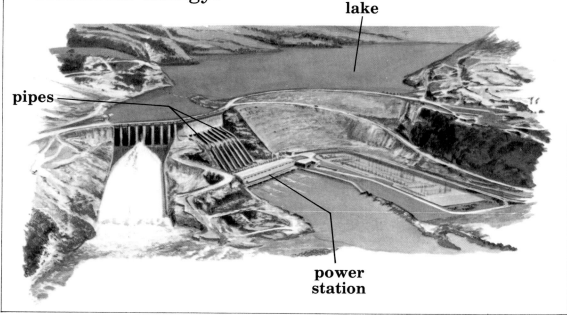

lake

pipes

power station

Several kinds of fuel are used in homes.
Coal, wood, gas, and oil can be used for
heating and cooking. Electricity can also be
used for heating and cooking. Electricity
gives us light and runs many household
machines. Without these sources of energy,
life would be very different.

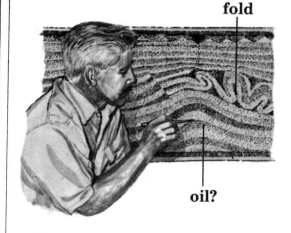

fold

oil?

Scientists are always searching for oil. They look for places where oil might be deep in the earth. They use instruments called seismographs to find these places. Then they study the seismograph records. Finally, they make a picture like this one. The picture shows a fold in the earth that might have oil.

There are many rocky folds in the
earth. But oil is not found in every fold.
Holes must be drilled to see if oil is there.
It may take a year to drill this hole. Oil is
sometimes found in distant places. It may
be found in jungles and deserts. The picture
shows drilling in Alaska.

pulley

extra
pipes

traveling
pulley

motors

drill bit

To get oil, drillers use a machine called a drilling rig. A motor turns a hollow drill pipe that pushes into the earth.

The work is done by a tool called a drill bit. The bit is at the end of the pipe.

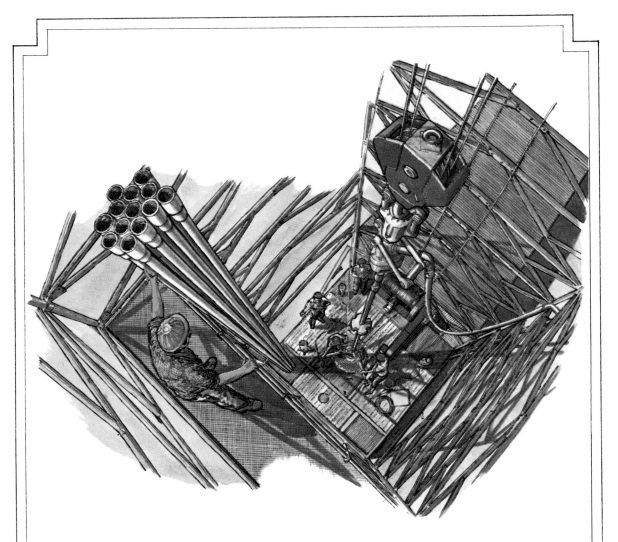

The drill pipe hangs from a pulley at the top of the rig. As the drill bit moves deeper into the ground, another pipe is added at the top. In this picture, you are looking down inside the rig.

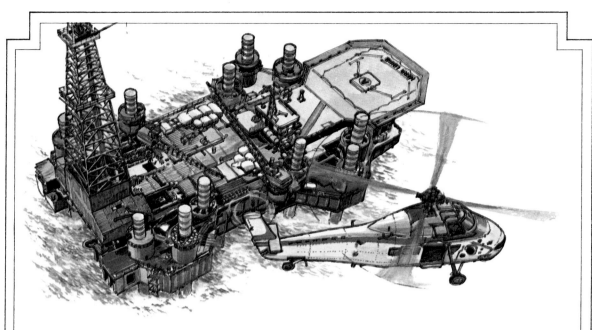

One of our best fuels is natural gas.
This gas is often found when drillers are
looking for oil. It may be found under land
or under the sea. To find gas or oil under
the sea, drillers use a special rig.
When oil or gas is
found, divers fit pipes
to the well. The pipes
carry the fuel to shore.

Oil and gas may be found in countries that do not need them. Then these countries sell the fuels to countries that do need them. Big ships called tankers carry the oil or gas across the sea. Pipes on land carry the oil and gas from the tankers to storage tanks on shore.

giant
oil tanker

Oil that comes out of the earth must be refined, or changed, so it can be used. First it is taken to an oil refinery.

In the refinery, the oil is changed to fuels such as gasoline, liquid gas, and heating oil. The refinery makes it possible for us to use most of the energy of oil as fuel.

We use the energy of oil in many ways. Our cars run on gasoline. Jet planes use a fuel called kerosene. Trucks, trains, and ships use diesel oil. We heat our buildings and run some of our electric power stations with oil. All of our machines need oil.

waterwheel   windmill   water turbine

The pictures show different kinds of
machines. The waterwheel and water
turbine get their power from moving water.
The windmill gets its power from the wind.
Steam gets its power from heated water.

early steam engine   steam turbine

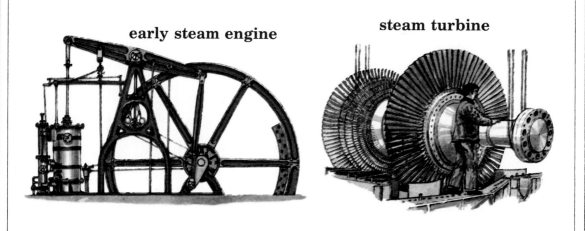

28

car's gasoline engine

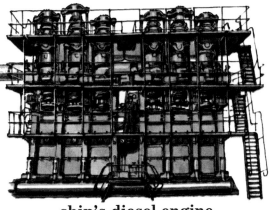
ship's diesel engine

Here are four kinds of modern engines. Each one needs a fuel. Each burns fuel to get energy so it can do work. The work these engines do is moving cars, ships, or airplanes.

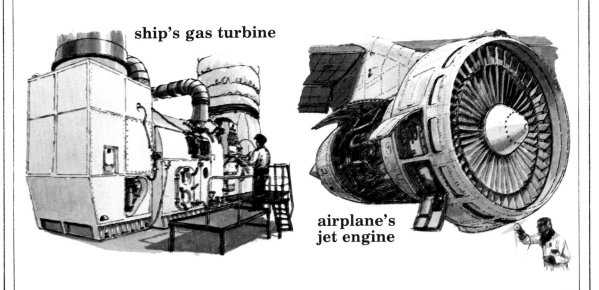
ship's gas turbine

airplane's jet engine

Spaceships use rocket engines. They get their energy from a fuel called liquid oxygen. This fuel burns very quickly and makes the rocket move very fast. The picture shows a big rocket taking off. The spaceship at the top of the rocket will go to the moon.

Spaceships need energy to do their work. They get it from electricity. They carry solar batteries that make electricity from sunlight.

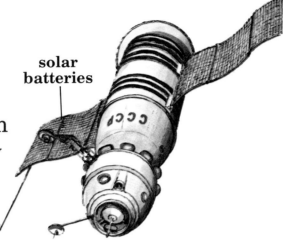

solar batteries

Spaceships that travel beyond the moon need a fuel that lasts longer than rocket fuel. They have engines that run on atomic fuels. Atomic engines can move giant spaceships to other planets.

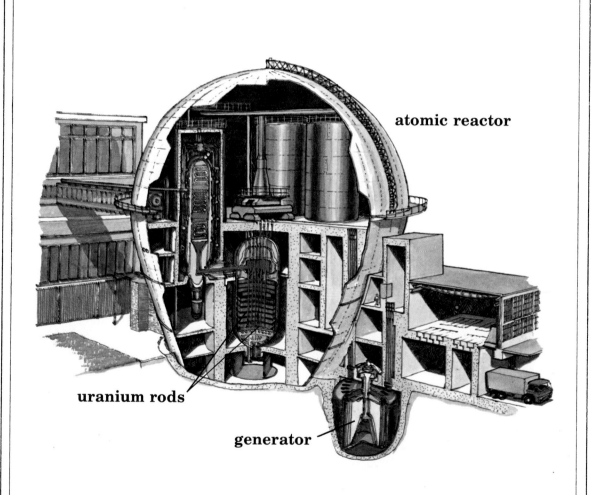

atomic reactor

uranium rods

generator

Someday coal, gas, and oil will be used up. So it is important to find new fuels. One answer to the problem is to use the energy of atoms. Atomic energy is made in an atomic reactor. The energy of uranium is used. The reactor produces heat by splitting uranium atoms. The heat runs a generator that makes electricity.

Putting atoms together is called fusion. Fusion produces even more heat than splitting atoms. The heat from fusion can be held in a special generator. The generator makes electricity.

The Metric System

In the United States, things are measured in inches, pounds, quarts, and so on. Most countries of the world use centimeters, kilograms, and liters for these things. The United States uses the American system to measure things. Most other countries use the metric system. By 1985, the United States will be using the metric system, too.

In some books, you will see two systems of measurement. For example, you might see a sentence like this: "That bicycle wheel is 27 inches (69 centimeters) across." When all countries have changed to the metric system, inches will not be used any more. But until then, you may sometimes have to change measurements from one system to the other. The chart on the next page will help you.

All you have to do is multiply the unit of measurement in Column 1 by the number in Column 2. That gives you the unit in Column 3.

Suppose you want to change 5 inches to centimeters. First, find inches in Column 1. Next, multiply 5 times 2.54. You get 12.7. So, 5 inches is 12.7 centimeters.

Column 1	Column 2	Column 3
THIS UNIT OF MEASUREMENT	TIMES THIS NUMBER	GIVES THIS UNIT OF MEASUREMENT
inches	2.54	centimeters
feet	30.	centimeters
feet	.3	meters
yards	.9	meters
miles	1.6	kilometers
ounces	28.	grams
pounds	.45	kilograms
fluid ounces	.03	liters
pints	.47	liters
quarts	.95	liters
gallons	3.8	liters
centimeters	.4	inches
meters	1.1	yards
kilometers	.6	miles
grams	.035	ounces
kilograms	2.2	pounds
liters	33.8	fluid ounces
liters	2.1	pints
liters	1.06	quarts
liters	.26	gallons

WORLD FUEL PRODUCTION

Source: US Department of Economic and Social Affairs

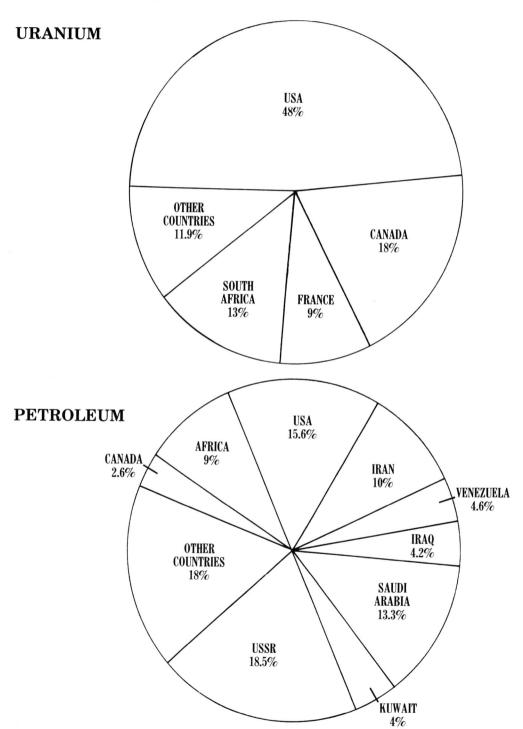

URANIUM

USA
48%

OTHER
COUNTRIES
11.9%

CANADA
18%

SOUTH
AFRICA
13%

FRANCE
9%

PETROLEUM

USA
15.6%

AFRICA
9%

CANADA
2.6%

IRAN
10%

VENEZUELA
4.6%

OTHER
COUNTRIES
18%

IRAQ
4.2%

SAUDI
ARABIA
13.3%

USSR
18.5%

KUWAIT
4%

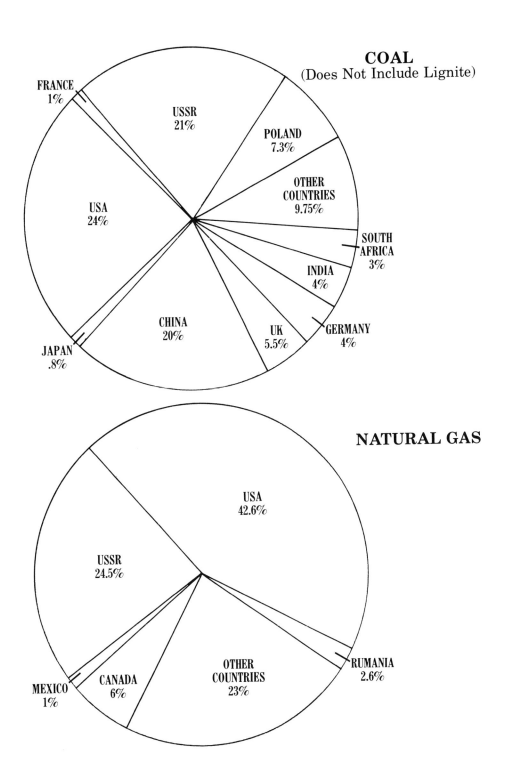

COAL
(Does Not Include Lignite)

FRANCE 1%

USSR 21%

POLAND 7.3%

OTHER COUNTRIES 9.75%

SOUTH AFRICA 3%

USA 24%

INDIA 4%

JAPAN .8%

CHINA 20%

UK 5.5%

GERMANY 4%

NATURAL GAS

USA 42.6%

USSR 24.5%

MEXICO 1%

CANADA 6%

OTHER COUNTRIES 23%

RUMANIA 2.6%

Where to Read About
Fuel and Energy

Pronunciation Key

a	a as in **cat**, **bad**
ā	a as in **able**, ai as in **train**, ay as in **play**
ä	a as in **father**, **car**, o as in **cot**
e	e as in **bend**, **yet**
ē	e as in **me**, ee as in **feel**, ea as in **beat**, ie as in **piece**, y as in **heavy**
i	i as in **in**, **pig**, e as in **pocket**
ī	i as in **ice**, **time**, ie as in **tie**, y as in **my**
o	o as in **top**, a as in **watch**
ō	o as in **old**, oa as in **goat**, ow as in **slow**, oe as in **toe**
ô	o as in **cloth**, au as in **caught**, aw as in **paw**, a as in **all**
oo	oo as in **good**, u as in **put**
o͞o	oo as in **tool**, ue as in **blue**
oi	oi as in **oil**, oy as in **toy**
ou	ou as in **out**, ow as in **plow**
u	u as in **up**, **gun**, o as in **other**
ur	ur as in **fur**, er as in **person**, ir as in **bird**, or as in **work**
yo͞o	u as in **use**, ew as in **few**
ə	a as in **again**, e as in **broken**, i as in **pencil**, o as in **attention**, u as in **surprise**
ch	ch as in **such**
ng	ng as in **sing**
sh	sh as in **shell**, **wish**
th	th as in **three**, **bath**
<u>th</u>	th as in **that**, **together**

GLOSSARY

These words are defined the way they are used in this book

atomic fuel (ə täm′ ik fyo͞o′əl) a fuel
that uses the energy of splitting atoms;
atomic fuel is often used to run the
engines of spaceships

atomic reactor (ə täm′ ik rē ak′ tər) a
device in which atomic energy is made

bell pit (bel′ pit) a small hole dug
to get coal from the ground

coal (kōl) a fuel formed by heavy rocks
pressing on dead trees for millions of
years

coal gas (kōl′ gas) a fuel that is given
off when coal is burned

conveyor belt (kən vā′ ər belt′) a
moving belt used in a coal mine to carry
the coal to the shaft

dam (dam) a wall that prevents water
from flowing

diatom (dī′ ə täm) any one of the tiny

sea creatures that turned into oil
after millions of years of being in folds
of rock

diesel oil (dē′ zəl oil′) a fuel often used
in trains, trucks, ships, and cars

drilling rig (dril′ ing rig′) a frame that
holds a drill used to make holes in the
earth from which oil is taken

energy (en′ ər jē) the ability to do work

fantail (fan′ tāl) the part of a windmill
that keeps the sails facing into the wind

fold (fōld) a layer of rock in the earth
where oil is often found

fuel (fyoo′ əl) any substance that burns
and gives energy

fusion (fyoo′ zhən) putting atoms
together; fusion produces a great
amount of heat energy

generator (jen′ ə rāt′ ər) a machine
that produces electricity

grindstone (grīnd′ stōn) a circular
stone, used in a windmill to grind grain

kerosene (ker′ ə sēn′) a fuel used in jet airplanes

lever (lev′ ər) a simple machine that makes it easier to lift things

liquid oxygen (lik′ wid äk′ sə jən) a fuel used to give energy to rocket engines

machine (mə shēn′) a device that makes work easier

mine (mīn) a pit in the earth from which coal is taken

natural gas (nach′ ər əl gas′) a fuel found deep in the earth or underwater; natural gas is often found with oil

oar (ôr) a lever used to pull a boat through water

oil (oil) a liquid fuel that is buried deep in the earth

pit prop (pit′ prop′) a support that holds up the roof of a coal mine

pulley (pool′ ē) a small wheel with ropes that makes it easier to lift an object

pyramid (pir′ ə mid) a large, ancient structure that has a square base and four triangular walls that meet at the top

ramp (ramp) a sloping floor that makes it easier to move things from one level to another

refine (ri fīn′) to change oil that comes from the ground so that it can be used as fuel

refinery (ri fī′ nər ē) a place where oil is refined

rocket engine (rok′ it en′ jin) an engine used to power spaceships

roller (rō′ lər) a turning cylinder that makes it easier to move something

rudder (rud′ ər) a lever that is used to steer a ship

seismograph (sīz′ mə graf) an instrument that measures vibrations and can help scientists find oil in the ground

solar battery (sō′ lər   bat′ ər ē) a
   battery that changes light from the sun
   into electricity

steam (stēm) the vapor that is formed
   when water is boiled

steam engine (stēm′   en′ jin) an engine
   that gets its power from changing water
   to steam

tanker (tang′ kər) a large ship used to
   carry oil or gas across the sea

turbine (tur′ bin) a machine that turns
   a generator, which then produces
   electricity

uranium (yoo rā′ nē əm) an element
   that supplies energy for an atomic
   reactor

waterwheel (wô′ tər   hwēl′) a wheel
   that is turned by moving water

windlass (wind′ ləs) a kind of wheel
   that makes it easier to pull up an
   anchor

Bibliography

Boyd, Waldo T. *The World of Energy Storage.*
New York: G. P. Putnam's Sons, 1977.

Branley, Franklyn M. *Energy for the Twenty First
Century.* New York: Thomas Y. Crowell, 1975.

Dolan, Edward. *Engines Work Like This.* New York:
McGraw-Hill Book Co., 1971.

Gutnik, Martin. *Energy: Its Past, Its Present,
Its Future.* Chicago: Childrens Press, Inc.,
1975.

Israel, Elaine. *The Great Energy Search.* New York:
Julian Messner, 1974.

Lefkowitz, R. J. *Fuel for Today and Tomorrow.*
New York: Thomas Y. Crowell, 1975.

Ridpath, Ian, ed. *Man and Materials: Oil.*
Reading, Mass.: Addison-Wesley Publishing Co.,
1975.